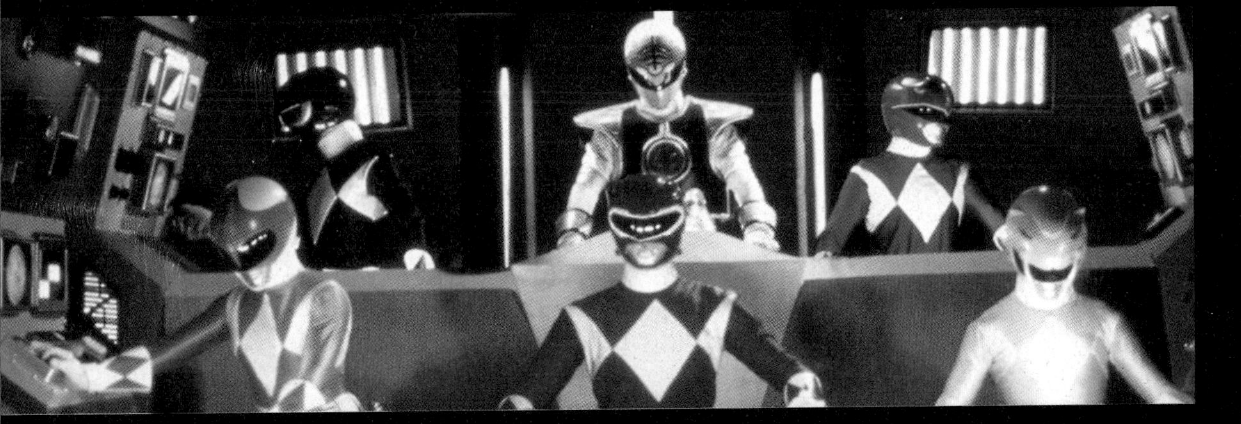

This book is packed with great features about us, our fighting equipment, our new Ninja powers – and even our Evil enemies (ugh!!). And it's all illustrated with a great collection of superb pictures taken on our adventures!

We hope you enjoy this awesome read!

We are Tommy, Billy, Katherine, Adam, Aisha and Rocky–

THE MIGHTY MORPHIN POWER RANGERS!

£5.50
UK only

CONTENTS

Licensed by E.C. Licensing Ltd Written and edited by Century 22 Limited
Designed by D&P Associates Published in Great Britain in 1996 by World International, Limited, Deanway Technology Centre, Wilmslow Road, Handforth, Cheshire SK9 3FB.

Printed in Italy ISBN 0 7498 2808 0

IMPORTANT WARNING! IMPORTANT WARNING!
The Mighty Morphin Power Rangers are specially trained in martial arts. Do not attempt to recreate any of their routines, tricks or stunts. And never, ever practise kicks on your friends!

The story of THE MIGHTY MORPHIN POWER RANGERS

HOW DID IT ALL BEGIN? WHERE DID THE POWER RANGERS COME FROM? TO FIND THE ANSWERS TO THESE FASCINATING QUESTIONS WE MUST REACH WAY BACK INTO THE HISTORY OF THE UNIVERSE ITSELF...

It was a time when the future itself was in serious doubt...A time when confusion reigned...A time when a terrible war raged between the forces of good and the forces of evil.
Good was represented by a wise wizard called Zordon – a true champion of all that is good, just and honest in the universe.
Opposing him and representing the power of evil and all things bad was Rita Repulsa, a vile and ghastly creature with an overwhelming ambition to rule the entire universe – and a mind full of evil plans to help her achieve that end! Time and again Zordon fought off countless attacks from Rita. But then she began the most terrible interstellar war of all, in which many planets, moons – and even a few stars – were completely obliterated.

The battles raged for more than 2,000 years – but no victor emerged in all that time. Neither side would give way.

Sensibly, Zordon realised that things could not go on as they were, and he came up with a simple solution. He and Rita Repulsa would toss a coin to decide who would rule in future.

The coin was flipped, and

Zordon won. But still Rita was not satisfied – she demanded 'the best of five'. Zordon agreed, the coin was flipped four more times, and still he won!

He now had to decide exactly what to do with her. Despite all the battles that had raged between them; despite the fact that he knew Rita was evil through and through – Zordon's innate goodness would not allow him to harm his adversary.

So, instead of completely eliminating her and her evil sidekicks, he decided to banish them in a Zithium cylinder – a space waste dumpster – which was cast into outer space where it would drift for eternity.

With Rita Repulsa out of the way, the universe was at last declared safe once again – safe for children, safe for animals, safe for everyone.

The dumpster drifted for years and years, and for many billions of space miles. Then came the fateful day when it crash-landed on a small moon that was gently orbiting a rather beautiful planet known as 'Earth'.

The dumpster stayed intact on the moon for the next 2,000 years with the vile Rita safely sealed inside, while seething with frustration at not being able to perpetrate more evil and further the nasty ambitions burning within her.

But, as is their nature, the Earthlings became curious about the mysterious cylinder on their moon and a lunar expedition was mounted to investigate the phenomenon. Unfortunately the astronauts broke the first rule of space exploration – they actually opened the container. And Rita Repulsa was set free!

Being wise and far thinking, Zordon had actually anticipated that this might happen one day and had installed a secret Command Centre in the California desert. The Centre, containing a super computer and an

inter-dimensional communicator, was monitored by a small, alert android called Alpha 5 who immediately informed Zordon of Rita's escape.

Zordon realised this was serious. He knew the time had come when he would have to fight Rita Repulsa, and all that she stood for, all over again!

Zordon instructed Alpha 5 to discover the most powerful forces that have ever existed on Earth. They would then harness these powers to fight their formidable foe. Alpha 5 set to work, using the inter-dimensional communicator. He soon reported his findings back to Zordon. The two most powerful forces yet seen on Earth, he had discovered, were Prehistoric Dinosaurs and Teenagers With Attitude!

With the aid of the inter-dimensional communicator Zordon, collected some fossilised dinosaur remains from Earth and used them as the basis for five enormous fighting machines called Tyrannosaurus Rex, Pterodactyl, Triceratops, Sabre-Toothed Tiger and Mastodon – collectively known as the Dinozords. These amazing fighting machines were capable of working independently, or of interlocking together as the truly awesome Megazord

Next, Zordon instructed Alpha 5 to recruit five Teenagers With Attitude who would help in the fight against evil. He found them in a place called

Angel Grove. Their names were Jason, Trini, Billy, Zack and Kimberly – and they became the Red, Yellow, Blue, Black and Pink Power Rangers.

Zordon then assigned each one to a Dinozord and gave each a Power Coin and a personal weapon. And so, THE MIGHTY MORPHIN POWER RANGERS, the most powerful force in the universe, were ready to do battle against the evil Rita Repulsa and all that she could throw at them!

Frustrated by the Power Rangers' early successes against her, the Evil Empress redoubled her efforts and wracked her brain for a way to break them!

She suddenly hit on the idea of using an ancient Power Coin to turn a sensitive teenager called Tommy into the Green Ranger, an evil being who would destroy the Power Rangers from within.

But Tommy was a good person at heart. With immense determination and courage – and the help of Jason in destroying the Sword of Darkness – he freed himself from Rita's spell and subsequently became the sixth Power Ranger.

This development sent Rita into a furious rage and she launched even more savage attacks against the Power Rangers. Aiming her hatred at Tommy, the boy who had thwarted her, she almost succeeded in destroying his powers by the use of a green candle. But Tommy transferred his powers to Jason while his Dinozord was utilised by all the Power Rangers.

Observing all of this from a far off solar system was a certain Lord Zedd, an evil despot who decided to take over from Rita Repulsa. He was sure that he could do a better job and he consigned Rita to a space waste dumpster and despatched it into the farthest reaches of outer space.

The evil Zedd proved to be as good (or rather, as 'bad') as his word. With awesome power he proceeded to destroy all the Dinozords. However, the ultra-clever Alpha 5 was able to reconstruct them – using the broken fragments – as Thunderzords called Unicorn, Tiger, Dragon, Lion, Griffin and Firebird.

Zordon then recalled Tommy to the Power Rangers, as the White Ranger whose power source is the light of goodness which can never be broken by the forces of evil.

Meanwhile the forces of evil were about to become even more awesome and terrifying, when Rita Repulsa and Lord Zedd got married.

Soon after the wedding Rita's brother Rito Revolto arrived on the scene bearing a belated wedding gift of Tenga Warrior Eggs for the happy couple. The evil trio then set about plotting the demise of the Power Rangers. They assembled a new army of monsters which then defeated the Zords and destroyed the Command Centre.

Zordon came to the rescue by telling the power teens of the legend of the Temple of Power and of Ninjor, Keeper of the Temple, who forged the original power coins.

In their search for the Temple, the teens trekked across the dangerous Desert of Despair where they escaped from an attack by Tenga Warriors.

Eventually the Rangers found the Temple and met the Ninjor who decided they were worthy of receiving new powers, which enable them to fight with a new ferocity and skill when needed, and new Zords – The Ninjazords.

Outside the Temple they employed their new powers to defeat the Tenga Warriors.

The Power Rangers then returned to Angel Grove, ready once again to take on Rita Repulsa, Lord Zedd, Rito and all their gruesome cronies...in the ultimate fight against Evil.

IT'S THAT WEDDING!!!

EVIL BEINGS WILL NO DOUBT FIND THESE PICTURES VERY ROMANTIC!

GOOD GUYS WILL FIND THEM ABSOLUTELY REVOLTING! THE PUTRID PICS SHOW THE WEDDING OF THE GRIM AND GRUESOME LORD ZEDD AND THE EXTRAORDINARILY EVIL RITA REPULSA.

APART THEY HATCHED LOTS OF TRIALS AND TRIBULATIONS FOR THE POWER RANGERS...BUT TOGETHER THEY REPRESENT DOUBLE TROUBLE!

TOMMY - THE

Tommy's Power Rangers career began in the most incredible way, when he was caught up in a spell cast by the ghastly Rita Repulsa. She almost succeeded in using him (as the Green Ranger) to destroy the Power Teens once and for all!

Indeed, if it hadn't been for the timely intervention of Alpha 5, the Green Ranger would have

WHITE RANGER

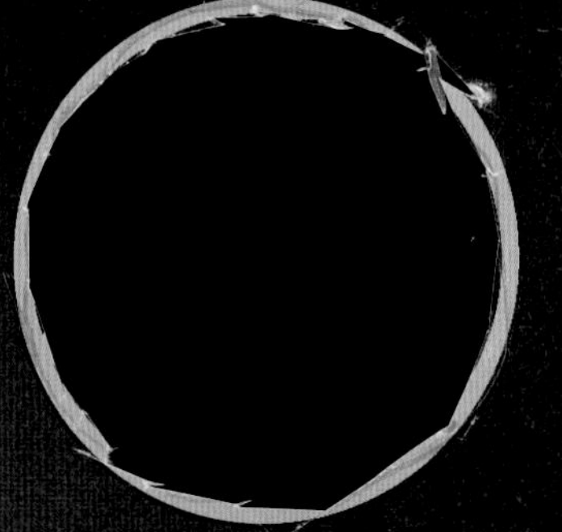

powers had been born of Evil, it was inevitable that they would one day fade. When that happened, Zordon transformed Tommy into the White Ranger...

succeeded in introducing a virus into the Command Centre's computer system.

As it happened, Alpha 5 trapped him inside a force field. This enabled the other Power Rangers to destroy the Green Ranger's Sword of Darkness – and Rita's spell was broken.

Tommy later thanked his new friends for saving him from the clutches of Rita Repulsa and the dark forces of Evil.

Meanwhile, Zordon was so favourably impressed with Tommy's true devotion to his friends, that he appointed him as the sixth Power Ranger.

Since the Green Ranger's

WHITE
RANGER'S
FALCONZORD
WHITE
RANGER'S
SHARK
CYCLE

FACTFILE
Name: Tommy
Age: 17
Birthdate: 20 September
Birthplace: California
Favourite food: Pizza
Likes: Music
Hobby: Song Writing
QUIZTIME
Q1. Who is Rita Repulsa's brother?
Q2. What did Rita's brother give her as a wedding present?
Answers on page 61
15

JASON DAVID FRANK as TOMMY

Jason David Frank – who portrays Tommy, the White Ranger, in *Mighty Morphin Power Rangers* – was recently voted 'one of the 50 most beautiful people of the year' by the prestigious American magazine *People*.

Jason was born in Covina, California, where he attended Bonita High School. He began his martial arts training as a four-year-old and eventually became a certified 4th Degree Black Belt.

He has now mastered all seven of the major styles of martial arts. He even began teaching the disciplines as a twelve-year-old, and still continues to tutor youngsters as often as he can.

Jason made his acting debut in *Mighty Morphin Power Rangers: The Movie*

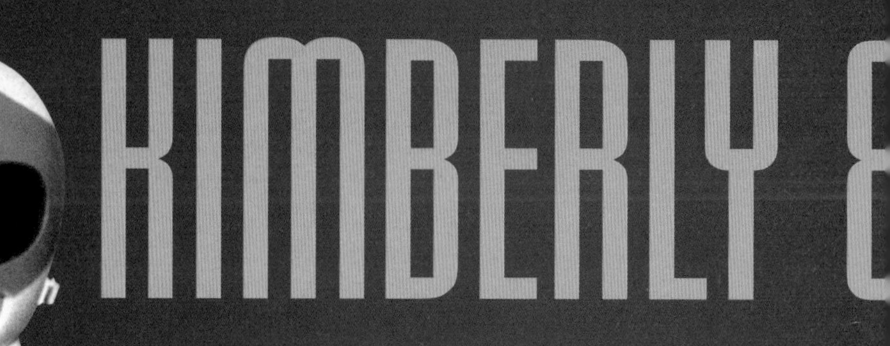

Katherine Hillard, the new Pink Ranger, is a bright and friendly newcomer to Angel Grove. She arrived in town when her father moved from Australia to take up a new job in the United States.

Unfortunately, her arrival proved to be just the opportunity Rita Repulsa had been waiting for and Katherine soon found herself under the evil spell of Rita and Lord Zedd.

KATHERINE THE PINK RANGER

They used her as a pawn in their endless, evil schemes against the Power Rangers

But good always triumphs in the end, and it was a good deed by Katherine which eventually broke the spell.

She became great friends with the Power Teens, and when Kimberly decided to pursue her dreams of becoming a world class gymnast, Katherine, was selected by Zordon to be the new Pink Ranger...

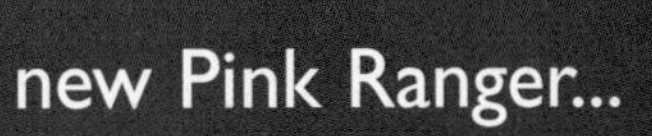

PINK RANGER'S SHARK CYCLE

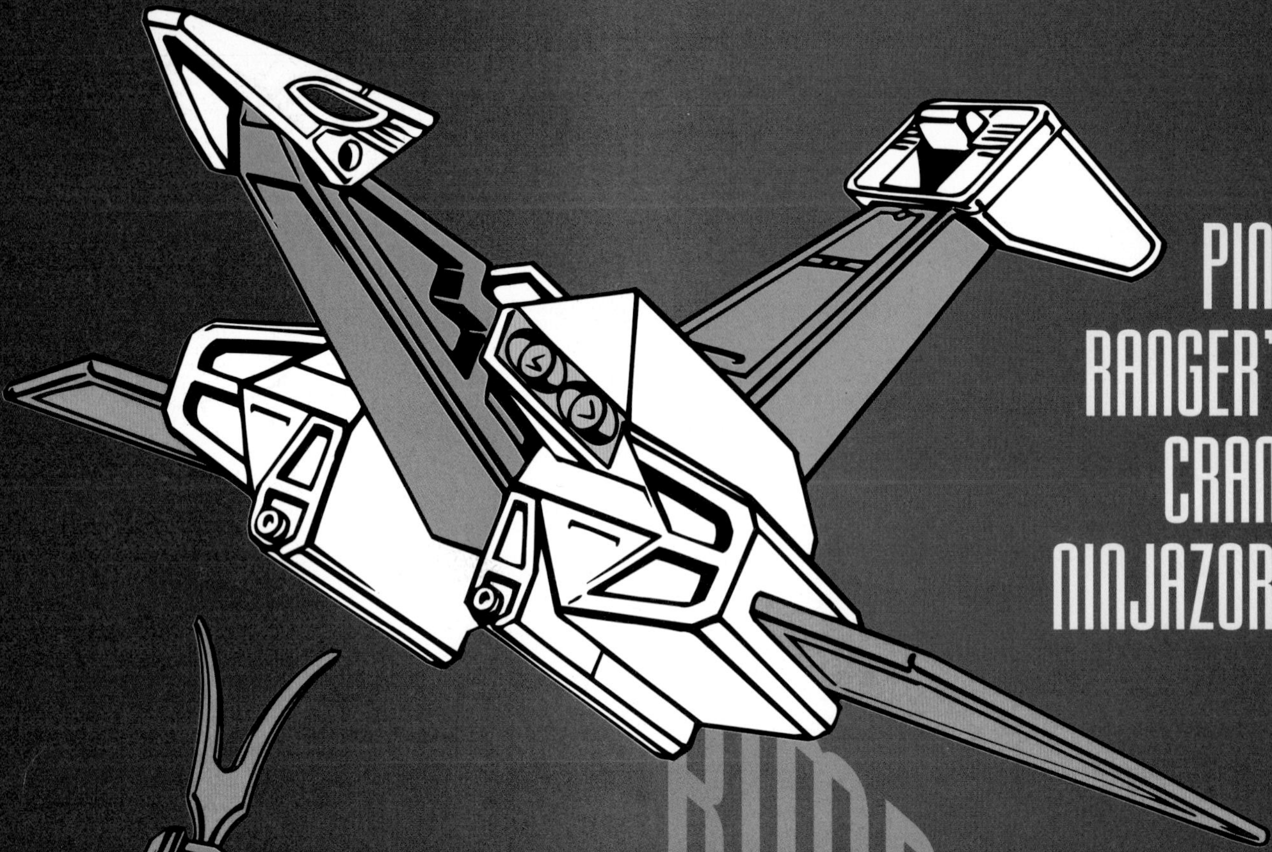

PINK
RANGER'S
CRANE
NINJAZORD

KIMBERLY
& KATHERINE

PINK RANGER'S
SHOGUNZORD

THE PINK RANGER

To which country did Kimberly's mother move when she remarried?

What is the name of Alpha 5's home planet?

Answers on page 61

Kimberly was brilliantly portrayed by Amy Jo Johnson, who became a great favourite with *Power Rangers*' fans everywhere.

Her replacement, Pink Ranger Katherine, is played by Catherine Sutherland, a native of Sydney, Australia – and a young lady who has been performing, in one form or other, for most of her life.

She began dancing at 4, playing the piano proficiently at 11, singing at 14 and acting at 16!

After graduating from the McDonald College of Performing Arts in 1992 she took acting master classes at the National Institute of Dramatic Art and at the Ensemble Acting Studios.

She has sung professionally, modelled, appeared in a number of commercials and was featured in a rock video.

Catherine first tried-out for a role in *Mighty Morphin Power Rangers: The Movie*, which was shot in Australia, but at the time she was considered too young for the part of 'Dulcea'. Fast forward in time, and she was eventually chosen to fill the role of the latest addition to the Power Teens of Angel Grove.

Landing the part of Katherine the Pink Ranger meant having to move away from her home and family in Sydney, to Los Angeles where *Power Rangers* is produced. "I miss my family a lot," says Catherine, "but we keep in touch by phone at least twice a week."

It was
farewell to
Kimberly, and
hello to
Katherine

ZORDON

ZORDON, THE WISE SAGE WHO BANISHED RITA REPULSA IN A SPACE WASTE DUMPSTER AFTER THE INTERSTELLAR WAR, IS WISE, KIND AND ALL-KNOWING.

He is a true champion of all that is good in the universe. He is also the creator of the Mighty Morphin Power Rangers.

Unfortunately, Zordon is trapped forever inside an inter-dimensional time warp and can never appear in person. He therefore communicates with the Power Rangers via his faithful servant Alpha 5 and the secret Command Centre in the California Desert.

NINJOR

NINJOR IS THE POWER RANGERS' NEW FRIEND AND ALLY IN THE FIGHT AGAINST EVIL. IT WAS HE WHO DEEMED THEM WORTHY OF RECEIVING THEIR NEW NINJA POWERS WHEN THEY LOCATED HIM IN THE TEMPLE OF POWER...

ROCKY - TH

RED RANGER

SEVENTEEN-YEAR-OLD ROCKY DE SANTOS IS A NICE GUY. HIS EASY-GOING NATURE AND READY SMILE MAKE IT VERY EASY TO LIKE HIM – AND EVERYONE DOES!

Rocky, who comes from a broken home, was raised in humble surroundings – and he had to help his mother to raise his six younger brothers and sisters.

It was originally to take a break from these family duties that he began to study martial arts. Now he's the proud possessor of a Black Belt and his fighting skills are truly awesome.

And, of course, Rocky has now become the second Red Power Ranger. He was chosen by Zordon when Jason became an ambassador for World Peace.

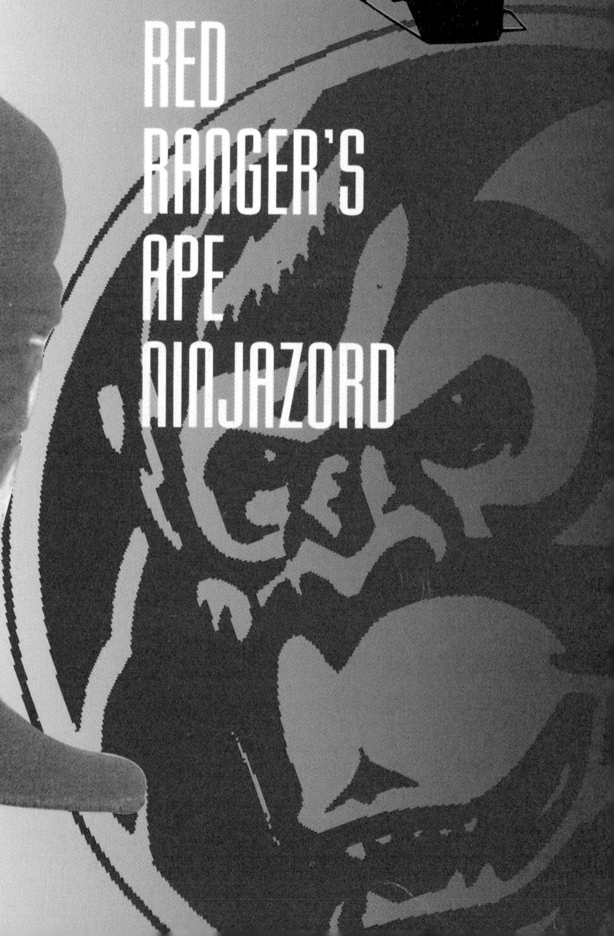

RED RANGER'S APE NINJAZORD

QUIZTIME

Q5. Who created Alpha 5?

Answers on page 61

RED RANGER'S SHOGUNZORD
RED RANGER'S SHARK CYCLE
QUIZTIME
Q6. What monstrous being was Mr Wilton transformed into?
Answers on page 61

STEVE'S MESSAGE TO HIS FANS
"Set a goal and follow through with it."

STEVEN CARDENAS, as ROCKY

Steve Cardenas, the top class gymnast who plays Rocky in *Mighty Morphin Power Rangers*, was born in Virginia. As a youngster he was introduced to the intricacies of martial arts by a former World Champion 7th Degree Black Belt, in San Antonio. Steve later won many tournaments, notably at the Idaho and Texas State Championships.

He then became a member of the 'Warriors', a demonstration team that travelled across the USA, helping and advising troubled teenagers.

His skills in gymnastics and martial arts led him to an audition for the role of Rocky De Santos. He won the part and, after shooting fifteen episodes of the TV series, he made his big screen debut in *Mighty Morphin Power Rangers: The Movie*.

Off screen Steve loves to draw and paint and says he would really love to own a world famous painting. He also loves to watch videos while eating popcorn!

FACTFILE

Full name: **Steven Cardenas**
Birthplace: **Virginia**
Birthdate: **29 May**
Weight: **150lbs**
Height: **5'8"**
Hair: **Brown**
Eyes: **Brown**
Favourite colour: **Navy blue**
Favourite actor: **Anthony Hopkins**
Favourite musician: **Jeff Baxter**
Favourite band: **Doobie Brothers**
Favourite food: **Mexican and Italian**

POWER RANGERS i

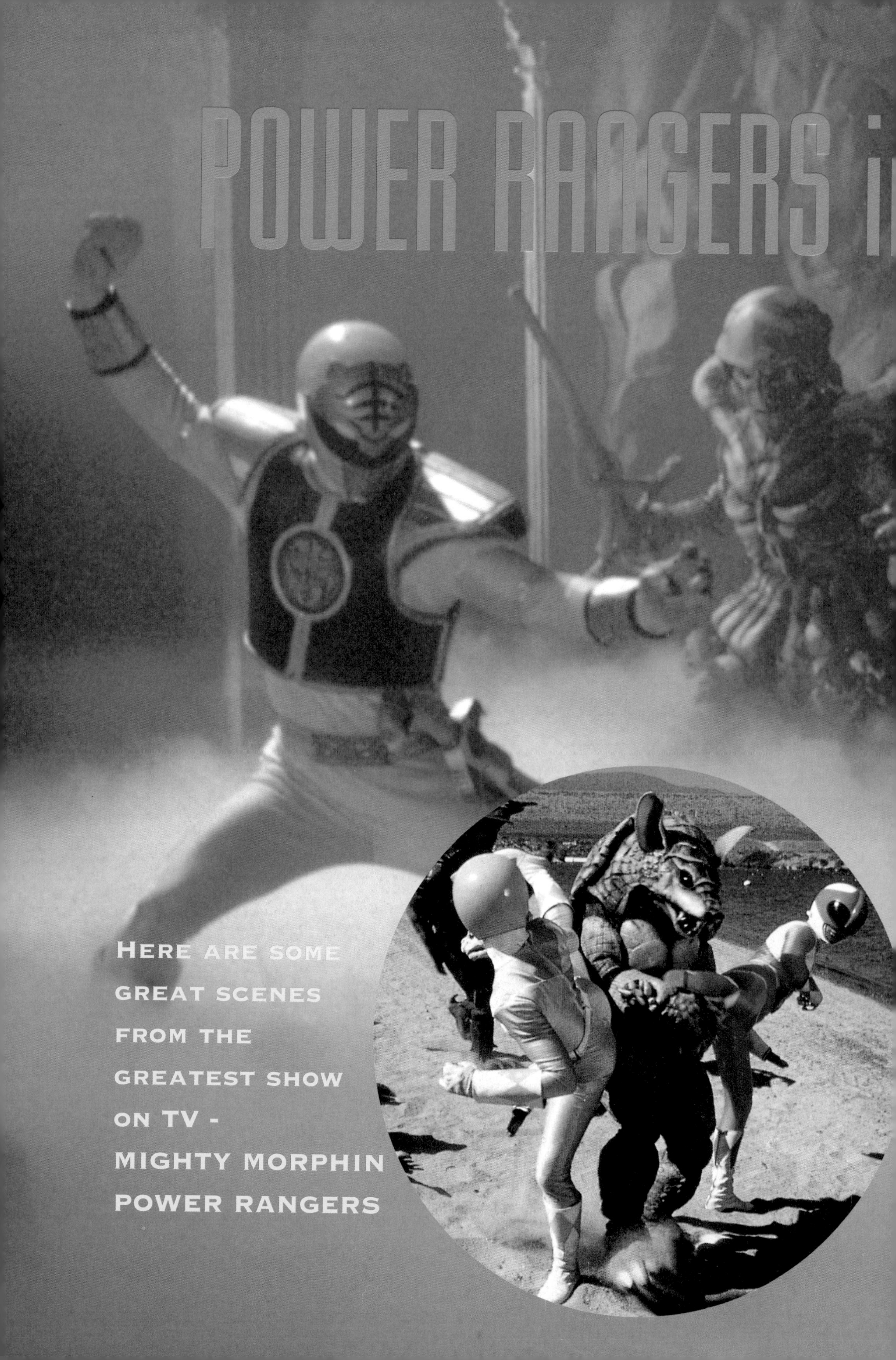

HERE ARE SOME
GREAT SCENES
FROM THE
GREATEST SHOW
ON TV -
MIGHTY MORPHIN
POWER RANGERS

AWESOME ACTION

GO, GO, POWER RANGERS!

BILLY - TH

BILLY, THE BLUE RANGER, IS THE BRAINIEST OF ALL THE POWER TEENS. HE IS INQUISITIVE ABOUT EVERYTHING AND JUST LOVES TO FIND OUT HOW EVERYTHING WORKS. HE EVEN ADMITS THAT LEARNING IS HIS HOBBY!

He's a real computer wizard, too; a king of the keyboard. In fact, his understanding of the inner-workings of the Command Centre computers has got the Power Rangers out of many tricky predicaments.

He's also pretty inventive – the wrist communicators and the Rad-Bug were both ideas of his.

BLUE RANGER

Because of Billy's super intelligence a lot of people find it difficult to get close to him. Many consider him to be a bit of a nerd. But once they get to know him, they quickly realise that he is a good hearted, good natured guy with a good understanding of almost everything!

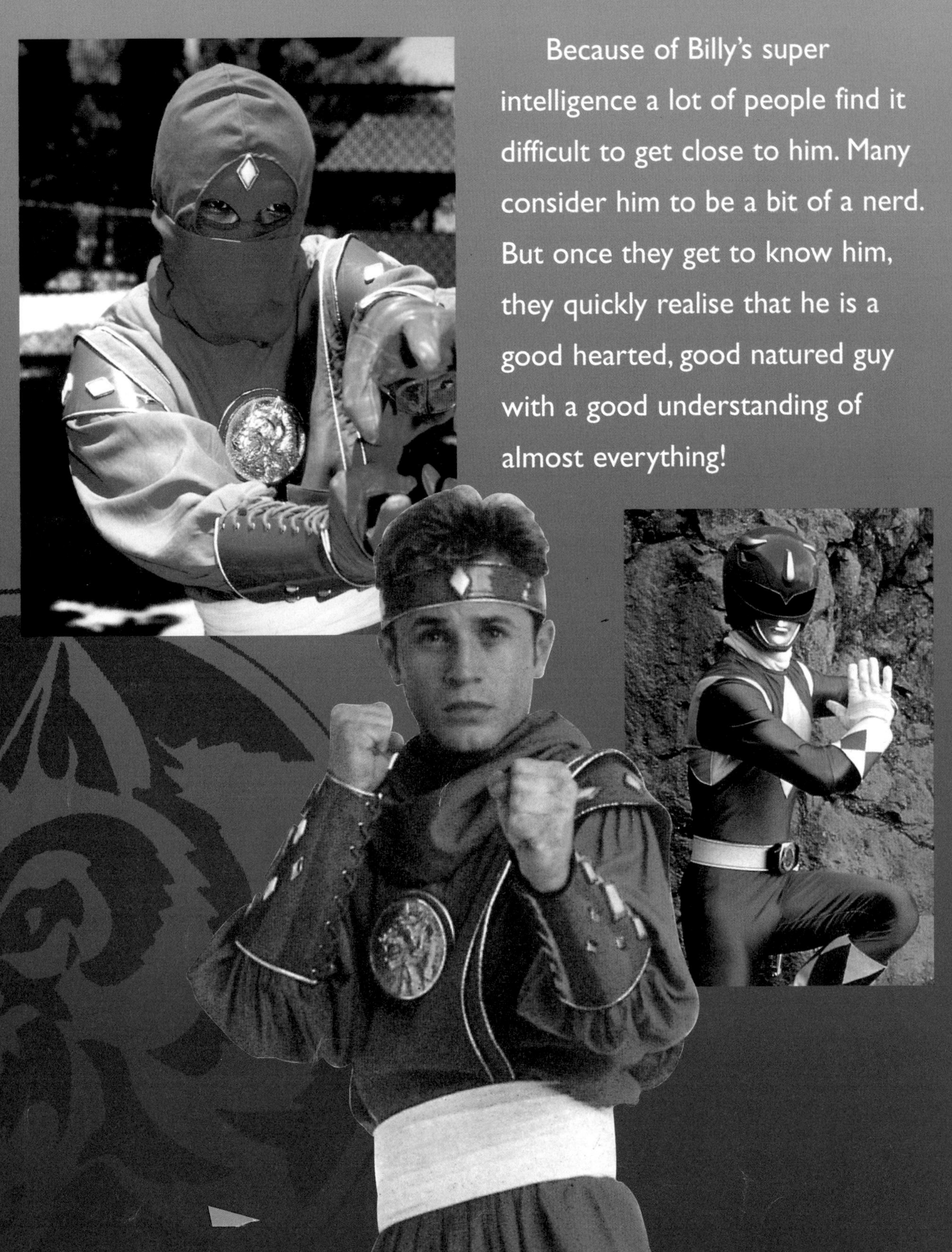

BLUE
RANGER'S
SHARK
CYCLE

QUIZTIME

Q7. Which monster turned people into footballs?

Q8. Which monster caused the Power Rangers to fight amongst themselves?

Answers on page 61

DAVID YOST, as BILLY

David Yost, who portrays Billy the Blue Ranger in *Mighty Morphin Power Rangers,* was born in Council Bluffs, Iowa. During his early childhood his family – his parents and an older sister – travelled all over the United States, a time he remembers as an amazing experience. It was as a child that he first had the ambition to become an actor.

After leaving high school David majored in Speech, Communications and Theatre at Graceland College in Iowa. Then, armed with a Bachelor of Arts degree, he moved westwards to Los Angeles to become a professional actor.

Eventually his acting and gymnastics skills helped him to land the plum role of Billy in *Mighty Morphin Power Rangers: The Movie.* Off screen David enjoys spending his time on the beach or jet-skiing on the ocean. Sometimes he goes off on hiking treks in the mountains. He also writes plays and screenplays.

FACTFILE
Full name: **David Yost**
Birthplace: **Council Bluffs, Iowa**
Weight: **135lbs**
Height: **5'7"**
Hair: **Brown**
Eyes: **Green**
Parents: **David & Cheryl**
Sister: **Chere**
Favourite colour: **Black**
Favourite actor: **Jack Nicholson**
Favourite actress: **Julia Louise Dreyfu**
Favourite TV show: **Married With Child**
Favourite band: **Hootie & The Blowfis**
Favourite food: **Mexican**

POWER RANGERS' PUZZLES

Solutions on page 61

MIGHTY MORPHIN WORDSEARCH

Find the 20 Power Rangers words listed here. They may be hidden forwards, backwards, up, down or diagonally

AISHA POWER WHITE RED
YELLOW ROCKY BILLY BLACK
RANGERS ZEDD NINJOR ZORD
TOMMY RITA REPULSA
BLUE TENGA SHARK PINK APE

A	I	S	H	A	P	O	W	E	R
R	S	C	B	X	B	O	H	A	A
W	S	B	I	L	L	Y	I	V	N
I	X	T	D	L	A	G	T	U	G
R	D	D	E	Z	C	D	E	R	E
E	G	Y	M	E	K	H	H	I	R
P	I	N	K	S	H	A	R	K	S
U	C	X	I	C	D	T	P	Y	J
L	J	D	A	N	O	I	F	E	K
S	X	E	G	Q	J	R	X	Z	U
A	K	F	N	Q	T	O	M	M	Y
B	L	U	E	L	Z	O	R	D	O
B	Y	A	T	M	O	W	V	Z	N

SPOT THE DIFFERENCES

Can you spot 12 differences between these great POWER RANGERS pictures?

These are the amazing Megazords produced when the Power Rangers morph together for extra power...

Shogun Megazord includes five Shogunzords plus the Power Sword...

SHOGUN MEGAZORD & NINJA MEGAFALCONZORD

Ninja Megafalconzord is morphed from the Ape Ninjazord, the Crane Ninjazord, the Frog Ninjazord, the Bear Ninjazord and the Wolf Ninjazord – plus Blue Ranger's Power Gloves...

AISHA – THE YELLOW

WHEN TRINI BECAME A PEACE AMBASSADOR IN SWITZERLAND, (ALONG WITH ZACK AND JASON) SHE WAS REPLACED AS THE YELLOW RANGER BY PRETTY AISHA CAMPBELL.

With her bubbly, live-wire personality, Aisha quickly established herself among the Power Teens, and she became best friends with Kimberly with whom she shared a tremendous passion for fashion!

Aisha is a very determined girl with strong opinions who will invariably speak her mind – and let you know exactly what she thinks.

RANGER

YELLOW RANGER'S SHARK CYCLE

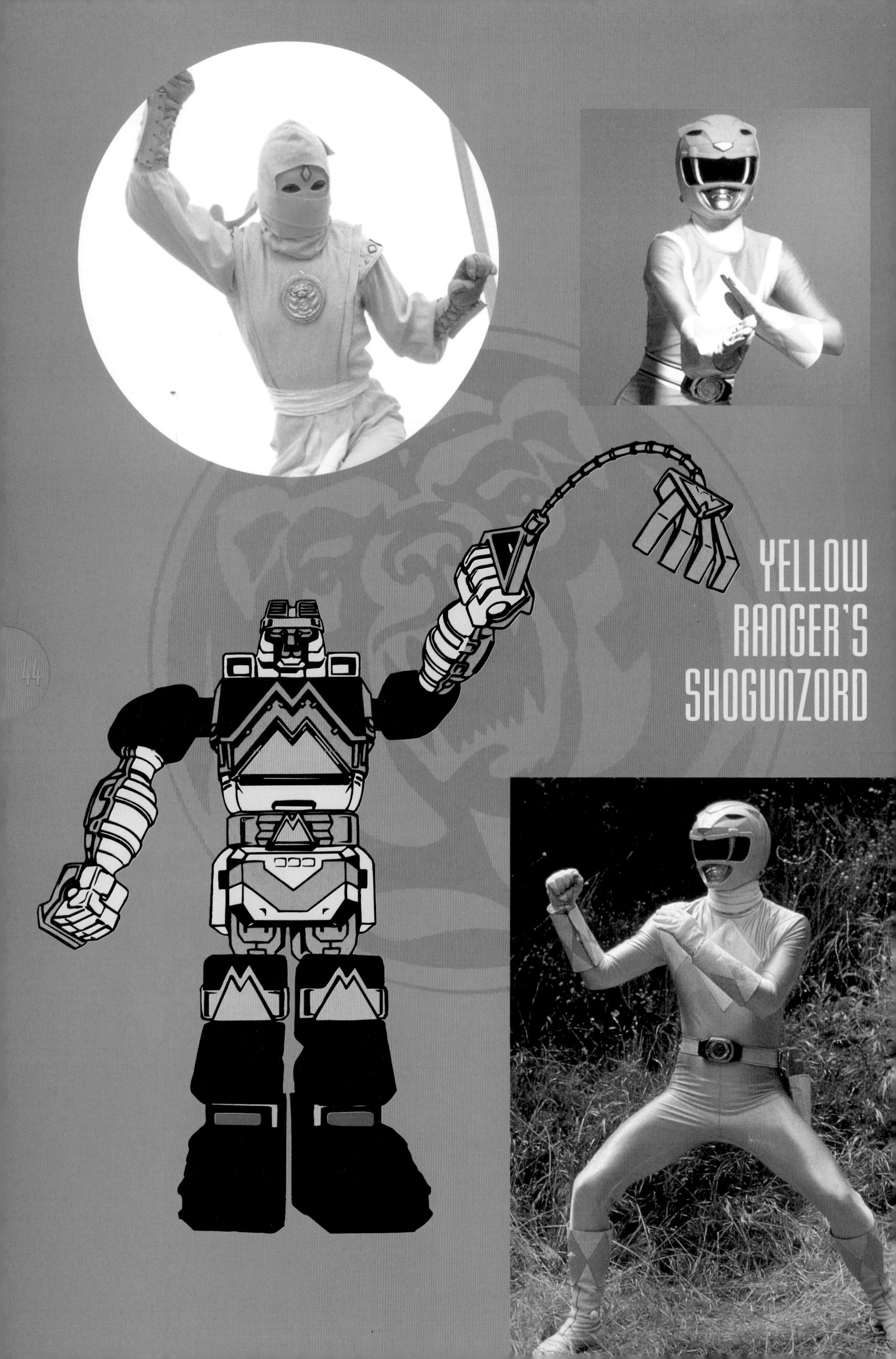

YELLOW RANGER'S SHOGUNZORD

YELLOW RANGER'S BEAR NINJAZORD

QUIZTIME

Q9. Who was the original Yellow Ranger?

Q10. Who were the legion of foot-soldiers created by Finster?

Answers on page 61

KARAN ASHLEY as AISHA

Aisha – the Yellow Power Ranger, is portrayed by Karan Ashley, a brilliant hip-hop dancer.
Karan was born in Odessa, Texas, but raised in Dallas along with her two sisters, six step-sisters and two step-brothers. She says her family is her most prized possession of all.

Among her happiest childhood memories is that of making her stage debut in a kindergarten musical. The acting bug obviously bit deep, as she made her first professional appearance at 13!

For five years Karan was a singer with rhythm & blues band Krush. Their single "Let's Get Together" was featured on the soundtrack of the brilliant movie *Mo' Money*. She has acted in TV show such as *Walker, Texas Ranger* and *Scratch TV*. She has been a model – and she's featured in numerous TV commercials in the USA.

But it was Karan's talent as a dancer that initially won her a role in *Mighty Morphin Power Rangers: The Movie*. In turn, that led to her TV role as Aisha – The Yellow Ranger in the most exciting show of them all!

FACTFILE

Full name: **Karan Ashley**
Birthplace: **Odessa, Texas**
Birthdate: **28 September**
Weight: **105lbs**
Height: **5'**
Hair: **Brown**
Eyes: **Green**
Parents: **Viola Cabera & Earl Jacks**
Favourite colour: **Black**
Favourite actor: **Denzel Washington**
Favourite actress: **Angela Bassett**
Favourite TV show: **Living Single**
Favourite band: **Boyz II Men**
Favourite food: **Macaroni & Che**

BULK & SKULL

Bulk and Skull first met in the maternity ward at the hospital where they were born. Every time Bulk cried, Skull cried too – and because of the noise they were isolated from all the other babies. The two have been constant companions ever since!

Bulk loves anything that makes a loud noise, and he loves to eat – he even holds the record for the most hot-dogs consumed by one person at the Youth Centre!

His constant sidekick, Skull, is a practical joker whose antics sometime create havoc around Angel Grove. But the laugh is usually on him in the end!

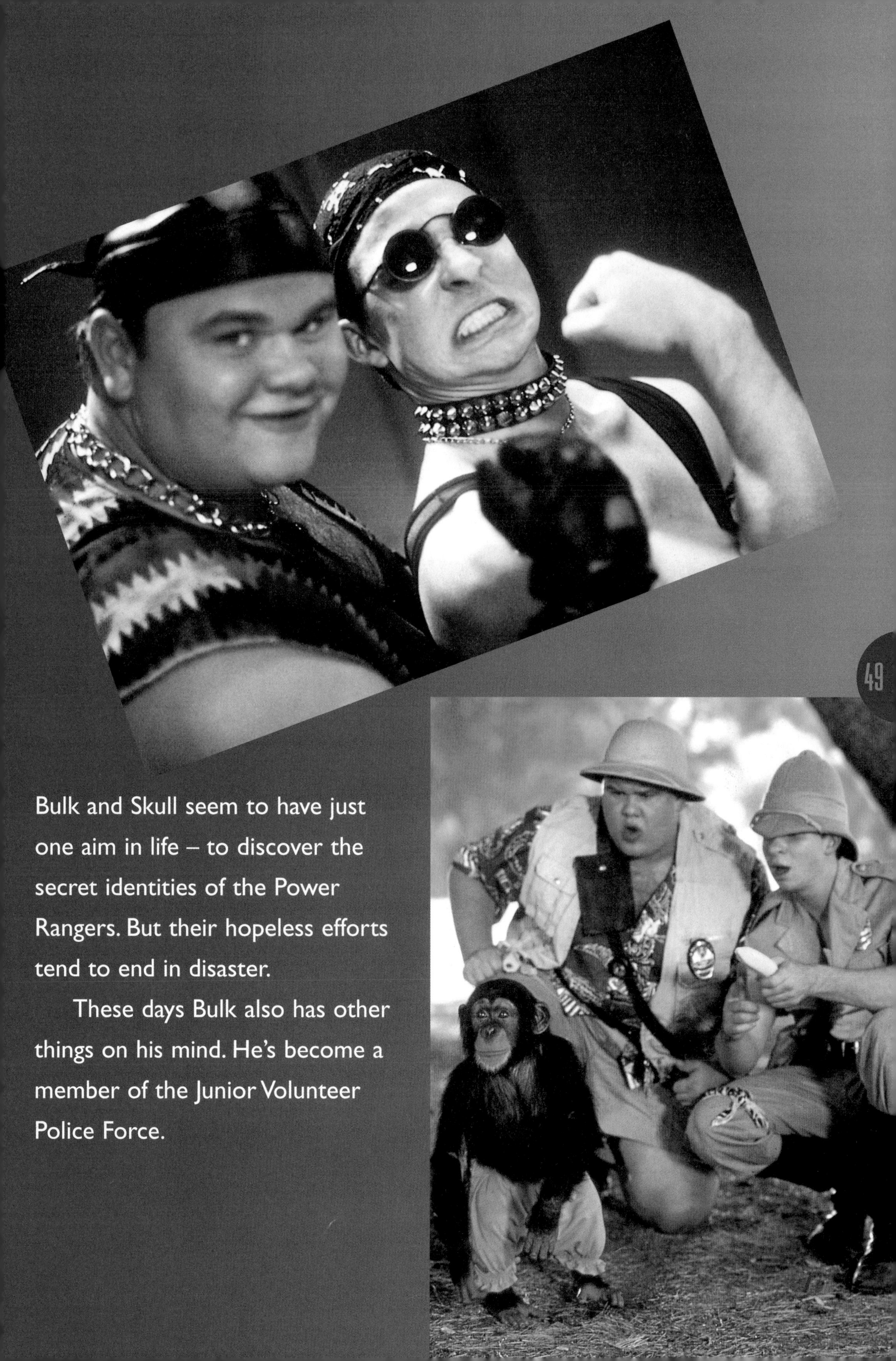

Bulk and Skull seem to have just one aim in life – to discover the secret identities of the Power Rangers. But their hopeless efforts tend to end in disaster.

These days Bulk also has other things on his mind. He's become a member of the Junior Volunteer Police Force.

ADAM - THE BLACK

When Zack left the Power Rangers to become a teenage peace ambassador, he was succeeded as the Black Ranger by 17-year-old Adam Park.

Adam, a good-looking Korean-American, had first become interested in martial arts as a rather shy youngster. It was initially a means of building his confidence and self-esteem – and as a defence against bullies who were invariably bigger than he was!

Adam has since put in years of dedicated training in a special form

RANGER

of martial arts known as Shaolin Kung Fu.

And many, many hours of Zen-like meditation have made him a very focused and disciplined individual with a tremendous inner strength. These qualities make him an ideal Power Ranger!

BLACK RANGER'S FROG NINJAZORD

QUIZTIME

Q11. Where did Zedd and Rita spend their second honeymoon?

Answers on page 61

BLACK RANGER'S SHARK CYCLE

BLACK
RANGER'S
SHOGUNZORD

JOHNNY YONG BOSCH as ADAM

JOHNNY'S MESSAGE TO HIS FANS

"Stay in school. Think positive. Don't do drugs. Follow your dreams."

ohnny Yong Bosch – Black Ranger, Adam, in *Mighty Morphin Power Rangers* – was born in Kansas, but brought up in Garland, Texas.

He first became interested in martial arts as a youngster, while watching movies starring such experts as Jackie Chan and Bruce Lee. "They were my heroes," he says.

For a long time he honed his martial arts skills by practising alone. After just a year-and-a-half he was proficient enough to win a coveted Purple Sash in Shaolin Kung Fu. He went on to achieve no less than seven competition trophies.

Johnny also loves soccer, a game he has played for the past ten years. This included four seasons at Garland High School where he eventually won the title of First Team All-District Forward.

Off screen Johnny likes to get away from it all to a place where he can: "See the stars and listen to nature."

ALPHA 5

AFTER THE ORIGINAL INTERSTELLAR WAR, ZORDON WISELY PLANNED AHEAD – IN CASE RITA REPULSA EVER ESCAPED FROM THE SPACE DUMPSTER IN WHICH SHE HAD BEEN BANISHED.

Zordon sent Alpha 5, a small, alert android from the planet Edenoi, to keep a look-out for her on Earth. He was stationed at a secret Command Centre in the California Desert, equipped with a super computer and an inter-dimensional communicator.

Alpha 5 instantly informed Zordon of Rita's escape on the Moon. In retaliation, Zordon instructed Alpha 5 to discover the most powerful forces that have ever existed on Earth, to use in his new fight against the forces of Evil...And that was how the original five Power Rangers were recruited.

These days Alpha 5 keeps an almost 'motherly' eye on the six Power Teens. He fusses over them and is constantly reminding them of what they need to do.

The Teens love him for it and treat him like a brother – a rather fussy one!

SHARK CYCLE POWER!

57

A GRUESOME

HERE ARE SOME OF THE HIDEOUS CREATURES ENCOUNTERED BY THE POWER RANGERS ON THEIR TRAVELS...

GALLERY

THE GRUESOME GALLERY CONTINUES OVERLEAF

A GRUESOME GALLERY

A	I	S	H	A	P	O	W	E	R
R	S	C	B	X	B	O	H	A	A
W	S	B	I	L	L	Y	I	V	N
I	X	T	D	L	A	G	T	U	G
R	D	D	E	Z	C	D	E	R	E
E	G	Y	M	E	K	H	H	I	R
P	I	N	K	S	H	A	R	K	S
U	C	X	I	C	D	T	P	Y	J
L	J	D	A	N	O	I	F	E	K
S	X	E	G	Q	J	R	X	Z	U
A	K	F	N	Q	T	O	M	M	Y
B	L	U	E	L	Z	O	R	D	O
B	Y	A	T	M	O	W	V	Z	N

PUZZLE SOLUTIONS

from page 40 and **QUIZ** running through book

Q1. Rito Revolto
Q2. Tenga Warrior eggs
Q3. France
Q4. Edenoi
Q5. Lexian
Q6. Marvo the Meanie

Q7. Centiback
Q8. The Hate Monster
Q9. Trini
Q10. The Putties
Q11. In Serpenterra
Q12. Zack